The Space Between

the Space Between

Meg Grehan

Little Island

The Space Between
First published in 2017 by
Little Island Books
7 Kenilworth Park
Dublin 6W
Ireland

ISBN: 978-1-910411-59-9

A British Library Cataloguing in Publication record for this book
is available from the British Library.

Cover illustration by Paula McGloin
Printed in Poland by Drukarnia Skleniarz

Little Island receives financial assistance from The Arts
Council/An Chomhairle Ealaíon and the Arts Council of
Northern Ireland

10 9 8 7 6 5 4 3 2 1

For Ci
Of course

The Shadows

The Shadows had a busy day
From beneath the blankets
She watched them work
Their way across the room

31st December

She sat at the kitchen table
Her mug making a circle on the wood
Tea steaming up her vision
It was dark
And stormy
And cold
And there were two hours left
In the day
In the year
In this
Terrible
Year
She had hoped that she would be happy
To see the end of it
That she could
Make a resolution
And start over
New for new
But she felt
Like a ragdoll
Missing stuffing
She felt
Like she had forgotten the combination
To everything she was
Like she had walked her way through the year
Dropping pieces of herself as she went
And now
Here she was

And what was left
Left over
Left behind
The last bits she clung to
Afraid that if they fell
That
Would be
That
That
Would be
The end
And so she decided

I Am

Panic was seeping in
A heavy fog
Too thick to see through
Making everything
Look wrong
Look ominous
Turning full stops to question marks

I am Beth
She told herself
I am Beth
She told the fog now rolling around her head
I am Beth

There was a buzzing
Coming from the inside
Out
Deafening
Turning everything to nothing

I am Beth
And I am
Here

She was in there somewhere
She just didn't know where

I am
Beth
I am
Right
Here

6am

It was 6am and she was awake

It was quiet
So quiet that she was sure she could hear her own
Heart
Beat
Thumping
Along

The alarm was set for 8am
The alarm was always set for 8am

It was 6am

Dark and Quiet and Cold

It was dark and quiet and cold
She tucked her knees up into her chest
Rubbing her feet together
Forcing a little heat into her bones

The heating was set to come on at 7:30am
Always 7:30am

But it was 6am

There's nothing planned for 6am

No ritual, no routine
6am was for sleeping
The day shouldn't start for two more hours

Two Whole Hours

She squeezed her eyes shut and started
Counting

One
Two
Go back to sleep
Three
Please
Four five six
Too early

Seven eight
Just until eight
Nine
This isn't part of it
Ten
This isn't part of it
Eleven
This isn't it
Twelve
This isn't
Thirteen
This
Fourteen
This is
Fifteen
Wrong
Sixteen
This is wrong
Seventeen
This isn't how it goes
Eighteen
You're ruining it
Nineteen
You're ruining everything
Twenty

You're doing it again

She gave up on counting but kept her eyes squeezed
closed
so tightly that she started to see blobs

floating on the pink tinged darkness of her eyelids

She watched them

There's a routine, there's a system
There's a reason for that system
Consistency is key
Consistency isn't scary
Consistency is safe

Just do the same thing
at the same time
just do it again and
again and again and
again and again and
again and again and
again until it sinks in
until your brain accepts it
until you can pretend
until you can pass as a person

A person with thoughts and feelings that aren't just fear
and fear and
fear and fear
and fear

Just keep going
Just keep going

Her head was starting to feel fuzzy
The cold air was getting harder to suck

into her
desperate
lungs

The plan

The Plan

Keeping her eyes shut so tight a little bit of her worried
that her eyelids would curl in on each other

She started murmuring to the room

8am wake up,
she told the wardrobe,
put on socks (the purple ones)
go to the bathroom
pee
wash your hands
wash your face
brush your hair

Go downstairs, she told the small desk,
boil the kettle
check the heating
light the fire
clean last night's dishes
coffee (milk, no sugar)
breakfast (toast with butter and strawberry jam)
in front of the fire

9am clear up, she told the chair,
wash the plate
wash the mug
wash the knife
wash the spoon
dry and put away
clean the surfaces with the spray that smells like apples

9:15am upstairs, she told the chest of drawers,
make the bed
lay out clothes for the day
(underwear, black leggings, tank top and a mustard
jumper and thick fluffy black socks) undress
fold pyjamas
put in drawer
get bathrobe from wardrobe

9:30am bathroom, she told the framed pictures on the
window sill,
a clean towel
hot water
shower gel (strawberry scented)
shampoo (for frizzy hair)
conditioner (matching)
face wash (sweet grapefruit)
hang bathrobe up on bathroom door
shower
body then shampoo then rinse then condition then
body again then rinse then face then body again
turn off shower

wring out hair
wrap up in towel
put on bathrobe
go to sink
brush teeth (three minutes)
mouthwash
floss

10am bedroom, she told the soft grey rug,
towel dry hair and body
deodorant
moisturiser on dry patch behind left knee
dressed
wet hair in a bun
hang towel over radiator
hang bathrobe on the door
sit on the bed

10:30am

                10:30

                                Ten thirty

Nothing

Her eyelids reluctantly cracked open
She checked the time again

6:12am

Great

She rolled over and tried to concentrate on breathing.

In.

Out.

In.

Out.

In.

    Hold.

        Hold.

            Hold.

Out.

She raised a hand and felt her cheek
It felt like marble
cold and smooth
She pinched her cheek lightly and felt a tiny spark of
   indignant heat under her fingertips

She sighed

'Ridiculous.'

She swung her feet out of bed
refusing to pick up the purple fuzzy socks

They were 8am
This was not 8am

She padded over to the mirror
A full length, white framed mirror
covered in tiny blue smudges
from the dozens of pictures that used to cover the glass
leaving just enough space
for it to still be deemed functional

She had taken the photos down the day she decided

She still wasn't completely sure
what she had decided

That she mattered more than anything else
That she needed
deserved and would take
the time
Pluck it out of real life
Take it for herself
A year in which nothing else existed
nothing was real
A year in which the decay
of relationships
of friendships
of every tiny component of a life
outside this house
wasn't important

A year with no expectations
no trying to squeeze her wriggling brain into a mould
That would allow her to go to school
to date
to have friends
to work in an office
to wear a pencil skirt
to complain about a hangover while chugging coffee from a to
go cup the size of her head
To drive a car
to impulse splurge at the supermarket
to travel
to have awkward encounters
to have meet-cutes
to complain about calories
to have weekdays
to have weekends
to have sick days and holidays and unplanned days
to have anything
To go outside
Did she matter?

Had she decided that she mattered
so much
that she could live in her own private world and let
everything
crumble around
her?

Or had she decided that she didn't matter at all
That she should close the door

let the world keep turning as she
crumbled?

She shook her head

'Shush,' she told her reflection sternly

6:21am

'Fine. Have it your way.'

She plodded downstairs and into the small
cosy sitting room that held
most of her life
The old squishy sofa
covered in so many blankets that she couldn't really
   remember what colour it was
under its plush rainbow coat
The bookshelves so tall she needed to stand tippy toes
on a beaten up old stool to reach the high shelves
The mantelpiece covered in knick knacks and candle
wax
The small coffee table that held a towering stack of
notebooks
with different coloured pages
poking out between almost every page
a mug so full of pens it was
practically impossible to put one back in
after you'd wrestled it out
The pictures on the walls
in brightly coloured frames

all screaming their beautiful
and only vaguely pretentious book quotes
in swirling letters

It was old but clean
beaten but loved and
everything she needed
It was her home

She ignored the caffeine deprivation
and the goosebumps
leaving the kettle and fireplace
until their designated time
and pulled the old stool over to the bookcase

The shelves were stuffed with books
some shiny and new, some well loved
some damaged from tears
or being thrown at walls
or being squeezed a little too tight
Many showed signs of all three

They were organised
They were always organised

'Morning,' she whispered, 'it's 6:30am.'

Her eyes ran slowly across the shelves
as though they weren't already intimately aware
of every single volume
as though she hadn't spent hours the night before rearranging

every single book
on every single shelf
for the third time
in as many days

She touched a fingertip to a spine
tracing the little cracked ripple from that page she'd
liked
too much to turn
She felt the smooth dust jacket of a hardback
that hadn't been opened
the soft blue ribbon poking out of another that had
been read
more times than she could remember

Eventually she stood up on the tippy-est of tippy-toes
closed her eyes
and ran a finger across the shelves until
something
told her to stop

She slid the tiny paperback out of its spot
tucked it in under her arm and hopped off the stool

'Hey,' she whispered, 'it's 6:36am.'

Together they flopped onto the squish mountain hiding
the mysteriously coloured sofa
She tucked herself in
wrapped her feet up in the softest blanket she could find
opened the book
and read

What Was

The bookshop was always just a little too warm
The smell of paper
People
And the heavy scent of coffee beans drifting
Through from the coffee shop next door
It filled the heat
Made it heavier
Made it a comforting weight
That held you, pressed against your skin
Welcoming you

The quiet was an unspoken vow
A promise to
The flipping pages
Whispers
Creaking of the old wooden floor
Under rain soaked boots
Dripping of sopping umbrellas left by the door
Always softly reminding you
That life went on
Time kept ticking
Outside of this tiny
Sanctuary
But always
Always reassuring
Proving
Here
You are safe

By February

The plan had grown
Stretched over the day
Taking over noon
Stretching into evening
It was getting easier
An hour of this
An hour of that
The same thing
Always
Every day
Every week
Food delivery on Saturday
The same
Meals at 8am
And
1pm
And
6pm
The same
It was easy
It was safe
It was quiet

Armour

The Decision had been easy to make
Barely a decision at all
Sometimes she thought maybe she called it that
Just to convince herself
That she had something to do with it

At first it was easy
It was relief
It was quiet and peaceful and open
All pressure gone
Her shoulders could roll without cracking
Her brow unfurled
She felt soft
Doughy
Mouldable

But
Day by day
It started to slip
To fall
To crumble

The armour rusted
No longer needed
Inside

The hinges loosened
Cracked
Plates fell away from each other
Paint chipped

Soon she was just
Her

No protection
No threat
No danger

Just
Her

No versions
No variations
No biting her tongue

No need to bite her tongue
No one to hear
No one to disappoint
No one

The person beneath the armour hadn't been seen
In so long
That she couldn't quite remember
Who she was

As the armour fell it felt like freedom

But as it crashed to the ground
Turned to dust
And left her
Soft and
Vulnerable

She started to see
She hadn't lost it
She hadn't slain the dragon
She hadn't saved the princess

She had traded it
For a tower
So tall
So thick
So impenetrable

That she started
To miss
Her
Armour

Crumpled

The box beneath the bed
Always had the lightest covering
A week's worth of
stubborn
Defiant dust
Sprinkled on top
Of a year of crumpled bank notes
Saved away
Hidden
Like acorns for winter
For pasta or beans or bread
For just
Enough
For one
For lights in the dark
And heat in the cold
A calculated
Wary
Amount
That relied
So heavily
On the sun rising
Lighting
And warming
That so many nights
Were spent
Staring into the darkness
Drowning in numbers

By March

The plan had turned on her

By April

The plan wrestled with her
Her aching brain battling for more sleep
For the inside of the sheets
For pillows
And darkness

By May

She was too tired
To fight
She went about the day
About the plan
With a numbness
A dullness
She did what she had to do
To keep feeling
Like a
Person
And not
For a
Single
Second
Did she care
Not for a second
Did she feel
Anything
At all

Day

Everything was heavy

The air felt muddy
The walls thick
The silence coated in lead

Her hands moved slowly
sluggishly
thudding onto her soft belly

Her fingers lay like small, smooth rolls of marble
cold

Her back sunk into the sofa cushions
all the way
to the ground
into the dirt
into the darkness
and that
was where she stayed

Heavy

Her head
started to feel too heavy to hold up
Everything seemed to get darker
like a shadow was slowly engulfing her

Her head felt heavy with whispers,
too quiet to fully make out but still deafening
somehow
It felt like the walls were sneaking their way closer to her.
She felt stuck
she felt like she should run but what would she be running from
and where would she run to?

The whispers grew louder
and louder and
louder
until
a low terrifying stream of sounds
too jumbled to make any sense
but dripping
poison
everywhere

What do you do when your brain is refusing to let you step outside
while screaming that you aren't safe
that you need to run
you need to go?

How do you stop the screaming when it's coming
from so deep inside?

The screaming started to quicken
started to deepen and
roll around the back of her head
She tried to breathe
to focus
but nothing cut through that
vicious river of noise
saying nothing but
shutting
everything
else
out

It hurt

A steamroller inside her head
crushing all of the willpower
the strength and the optimism
Eventually the last remaining fractured pieces of what
she could recognise as herself
gave in
gave up

The voice took over

You aren't
safe

You aren't
OK
Try all you want but let me ask you this:
What's the point?

Why even try?
Why?
What makes you think you can do anything?
What makes you think it's worth it?
What if you get better and it just

                                        comes back?

Maybe you could beat it
this once
but what about
Next Time
you definitely aren't strong enough to beat it again

and again
and again and again
and again and again and again
and again and again
and again
It will keep coming back
It's a part of you.
Who are you without it?
What would you do?
Even if you could go outside what

                            use
                        are you?
                                What more is there?

All you are is
Fear
you're useless
               pointless
                              stupid
                                              weak
You should just give up give in let it win
because you can't
You'll be stuck like this and
Everything
will be wasted on you
Every day of your life is
A Waste

Other people do stuff
They go places
They make things
You may as well not even exist
You do nothing
You are
Nothing

All you are is this and
                     even
                  you
                      don't
                          want
This

Things will never be OK. You will never be OK. You will never
win. You will always be

this

Pathetic

Afraid of
everything
nothing
Afraid of fear
A waste
    A waste of space
     A waste of time
       A waste of resources
      A waste of a body
        A waste of money
          A waste of energy
         A waste of a life

        Worthless

The screaming was so fast it was just a malicious wail
bouncing around her skull
beating and bruising
everything it came into contact with
turning her mind into a battlefield
Everything was too fast
it wouldn't stop
it just kept going
                and going
                      and going
Screaming so loudly
        so angrily

in a terrifying way
        calmly
        confidently

It knew it was right
It knew
She knew

She raised a fist and brought it
thundering down on her
forehead

Shut up shut up shut up shut up shut up shut up shut up
shut up shut up shut up shut up shut up shut up shut up
shut up shut up shut up shut up shut up shut up shut up
shut up shut up shut up shut up shut up shut up shut up
shut up shut up shut up shut up shut up shut up shut up
shut up shut up shut up shut up shut up shut up shut up
shut up shut up shut up shut up shut up shut up shut up
shut up shut up shut up shut up shut up shut up shut up
shut up shut up shut up shut up shut up shut up shut up
shut up shut up shut up shut up shut up shut up shut up
shut up shut up shut up shut up shut up shut up shut up
shut up shut up shut up shut up shut up shut up shut up
shut up shut up shut up shut up shut up shut up shut up
shut up shut up shut up shut up shut up shut up shut up
shut up shut up shut up shut up shut up shut up shut up
shut up shut up shut up shut up shut up shut up shut up
shut up shut up shut up shut up shut up shut up shut up
shut up shut up shut up shut up shut up shut up shut up

shut up shut up shut up shut up shut up shut up shut up
shut up shut up shut up shut up shut up shut up shut up
shut up shut up shut up shut up shut up shut up shut up
shut up shut up shut up shut up shut up shut up shut up
shut up shut up shut up shut up shut up shut up shut up
shut up shut up shut up shut up shut up shut up shut up
shut up shut up shut up shut up shut up shut up shut up
shut up shut up shut up shut up shut up shut up shut up
shut up shut up shut up shut up shut up shut up shut up
shut up shut up shut up shut up shut up shut up shut up
shut up shut up shut up shut up shut up shut up shut up
shut up shut up shut up shut up shut up shut up shut up
shut up shut up shut up shut up shut up shut up shut up
shut up shut up shut up shut up shut up shut up shut up
shut up shut up shut up shut up shut up shut up shut up
shut up shut up shut up shut up shut up shut up shut up
shut up shut up shut up shut up shut up shut up shut up
shut up shut up shut up shut up shut up shut up shut up
shut up shut up shut up shut up shut up shut up shut up
shut up shut up shut up shut up shut up shut up shut up
shut up shut up shut up shut up shut up shut up shut up
shut up shut up shut up shut up shut up shut up shut up
shut up shut up shut up shut up shut up shut up shut up
shut up shut up shut up shut up shut up shut up shut up
shut up shut up shut up shut up shut up shut up shut up
shut up shut up shut up shut up shut up shut up shut up
shut up shut up shut up shut up shut up shut up shut up
shut up shut up shut up shut up shut up shut up shut up
shut up shut up shut up shut up shut up shut up shut up

shut up shut up shut up shut up shut up shut up shut up
shut up shut up shut up shut up shut up shut up shut up
shut up shut up shut up shut up shut up shut up shut up
shut up shut up shut up shut up shut up shut up shut up
shut up shut up shut up shut up shut up shut up shut up
shut up shut up shut up shut up shut up shut up shut up
shut up shut up shut up shut up shut up shut up shut up
shut up shut up shut up shut up shut up shut up shut up
shut up shut up shut up shut up shut up shut up shut up
shut up shut up shut up shut up shut up shut up shut up
shut up shut up shut up shut up shut up shut up shut up
shut up shut up shut up shut up shut up shut up shut up
shut up shut up shut up shut up shut up shut up shut up
shut up shut up shut up shut up shut up shut up shut up
shut up shut up shut up shut up shut up shut up shut up
shut up shut up shut up shut up shut up shut up shut up
shut up shut up shut up shut up shut up shut up shut up
shut up shut up shut up shut up shut up shut up shut up
shut up shut up shut up shut up shut up shut up shut up
shut up shut up shut up shut up shut up shut up shut up
shut up shut up shut up shut up shut up shut up shut up
shut up shut up shut up shut up shut up shut up shut up
shut up shut up shut up shut up shut up shut up shut up
shut up shut up shut up shut up shut up shut up shut up
shut up shut up shut up shut up shut up shut up shut up
shut up shut up shut up shut up shut up shut up shut up
shut up shut up shut up shut up shut up shut up shut up
shut up shut up shut up shut up shut up shut up shut up
shut up shut up shut up shut up shut up shut up shut up
shut up shut up shut up shut up shut up shut up shut up

shut up shut up shut up shut up shut up shut up shut up
shut up shut up shut up shut up shut up shut up shut up
shut up shut up shut up shut up shut up shut up shut up
shut up shut up shut up shut up shut up shut up shut up
shut up shut up

Everything went
quiet

Her forehead throbbed
her chest felt too tight to allow air in
and she could swear
her throat
had
closed

She was too warm
She pulled off her socks as frantically as her exhausted body
and aching knuckles
would allow and placed her feet firmly on the
cold
wooden floor

She pulled off her T-shirt
wondering why she had ever thought such a tight neckline was OK

The way her sweaty hair
         clung
to the back of her neck
was enough to make her chest feel like it was caving in on itself

and she scraped the strands into a limp ponytail
struggling a little with
her shaky hands

Exhausted
she dragged herself to the kitchen
her mouth felt so dry that the panic tried to surge back up

– you're going to die you're going to die you're going to die –

she stuck her head under the tap, chugging as much
ice cold water
as she could
letting what escaped drizzle over her clammy face

Once her tongue stopped feeling like sandpaper
and she couldn't tell if the shaking was panic or cold induced
she checked all of the locks
trudged upstairs
and collapsed
into bed

Nothing Kind of a Day

It was a nothing kind of a day
Not a bad day
Or a great day
Just a day

She did everything she did
She read
She reorganised the bookcase
She wandered through the house
Saying a quiet hello to each room

Blowing away dust before it settled
Keeping her world
A world worth spending
Every
Single
Day
In

Tired

She turned a page
The swish adding a layer to the silence
The paper thick and smooth between her fingers
Heavy with words she was too sleepy to hold

It was dark
Outside
Inside
The lone lamp and the last of the flames
Warming the darkness, softening the edges

The day had been long
No longer than the one before
Or the one to come
But still
Long

Her eyelids were heavy
Dry
A dull metallic tiredness sat at the back of her throat
Her skin felt stretched
Dry
Her head
Just a little
Fuzzy

It was 10:27

Three
More
Minutes

Until
Sleep
Until
The End
Of the day
The

Long

Day

Three minutes
Reading
The same
Paragraph
The same
Paragraph
Once
Twice
Eyelids
Determined to
Meet

10:29
So
Close

10:30
Fold the blankets
Arrange the cushions
Mark the page

The floor was cold on the pads of her toes
The carpeted stairs calling

The quiet
Heavy with darkness and sleep
Broken
By
A

Snuffle

Tap

Scratch

Unprepared

A stiff shiver
Rolled its way down
Her spine
Poker straight
Rigid
Alert

Unprepared

Tip Toe

Tip
Toe
Eyes
Closed
Hands
Out
Grasping

Just reach

the staircase

Just get

Upstairs

Close the door
Keep your eyes
Closed
Shut
Tight
Just
Sleep

?

A Whimper
Inquisitive

A soft
oddly comforting
Whimper

Not sad
Just
A question

OK

The words she'd closed the door on
The words she'd banished
Tired of them surrounding her
Tired of not having an answer
Anyone would want to hear
An answer she wasn't ashamed of
An answer that wasn't just
A lie
A smile
Empty words
Words that gripped her stomach
Pulled her ribs in closer
Tighter
Crushing
Everything
Together
Words that proved
She
Was
Failing
That she was
Broken
And it
Showed
It was
Obvious
Words that betrayed everything
Words she hadn't heard

In months
Words she never wanted to hear again

Are

You

OK

But this time
Not words
No words
A Whimper
A Question

And for once
As she turned, opened her eyes
Made her way to the window
To the face full of questions
She answered
Honestly
With
A whimper

Meeting Mouse

Big eyes
Bigger nose
Round and soft
Plush like a pillow

Mouth open
Tongue lolling happily
Sharp teeth glimmering without a hint of menace

Ears flopped just a little
At the scrappy tips
Scruffy paws
Big paws
Too big
Awkward paws

That big face tilted just enough to say

Hey

What are you doing?

She smiled
She couldn't help it

'Not much.
You?'

She tapped the glass
lightly
With the pad of one warm finger
and a tail answered
back and forth as if powered by pure
excitement

She talked!

'What's your name?' she said
softly
as if expecting a reply
Soft words in a
Softer voice

A little silver bone shimmered as it swung
on a light blue collar
She couldn't make out the name engraved but at least
The sweetness had a home

'Where do you belong?'

A head tilt.

'Is someone missing you?'

A tail wag.

'Are you lost?'

That big nose pressed up against the glass
A happy breath fogging a cloud around it

She giggled
A real giggle
Full of heart
That gurgled up from somewhere
She'd forgotten

'Silly goose.'

Ears perked, head turned, tail wagged
Furiously, unquestionably happy

A voice from somewhere past the darkness
Called a name she couldn't hear
It sounded like a nice voice
Gentle

One last look from soft, dark eyes and a quiet
bark
Maybe a
'See you next time,'

and it was gone
and she was alone

Smiling at the nose shaped smudge on the window
That looked just enough like a heart

The Next Morning

She remembered the face
The big kind eyes
At first she thought
Maybe
It had been a dream

But when her cold toes tipped into the sitting room
There it was
The Smudge

She felt a little wiggle in her chest
A little tug on her lips
She touched the sloppy heart
And muttered a good morning

Crowded

The day she realised
How sad she was
Was the day
She was
Happy
Just
Happy and
Nothing
Nothing but
Happy
For the first time
In the longest time

There was music
It was loud
It thumped through her
Violent waves crushing through her body
People
Sweaty, dancing people
Screaming
A solid wall of sound

It was too much
It was everything she couldn't take
It was the worst
But
It was the very best

Because the noise
Was the song that she knew so well
The song that made the worst nights

Hurt a little less
The people
Were feeling everything she was feeling
She was alone in a crowd
She was invisible in the
Best Way

The screaming was excitement
It was happy
It was emotions that have no names
Emotions that can't be spoken
Only screamed from deep inside
The middle of a crowd of people screaming the
Exact
Same
Thing
Where no one can hear you
Because their own screams
Are just as loud
Just as heavy
Just as important

There was sweat everywhere
The air was hot and wet
Every breath sat in her lungs with extra weight
It was uncomfortable and awkward
Squished between strangers
With panic held down only by the desperate need to let go

Just

This

Once

Learning

The dog was back
and she couldn't help but be
so
happy
to see that face
peering in the window
every bit as happy

'Welcome back!'
A woof, a twirl
A paw on the glass

She could see the little bone twinkling on
    that blue collar
Mouse
Mouse

'Hi Mouse.'

Another twirl, a big happy mouth
pink tongue, shiny teeth

She opened the window and two scruffy paws popped
up
She reached out a hand
and got a quick wet lick

She scratched behind those floppy ears
Mouse leaned a cheek into her palm
looking right into her eyes
like a favourite toy
that had been lost for so long

After a little while
Mouse let out a soft bark and disappeared
Beth stayed at the window
She wasn't ready to be alone yet
She didn't want it
and she liked not wanting it

Mouse dashed back into the garden
proudly brandishing a
drool drenched bouncy ball

Beth laughed
'You're a smart little nugget, aren't you?'
She reached a hand out and Mouse dropped the
slimy toy right into her open palm
so excited that all four paws did an
elaborate tap dance on the wooden deck
little claws making soft clinks

She threw the ball
Not too hard
Not too far
She didn't want Mouse to go

A flurry of chocolate brown fur
gangly legs
too big paws
and the ball was back in her hand

and they played
she laughed
Mouse barked conversationally
and time went by
The sky turned pink
and neither of them bored of the ball
of the comforting repetitiveness
Beth would throw
Mouse would fetch
Reliable
safe
like everything she filled her days with
but this
this
this was different
this
this
was fun

When the sun set and
Beth had to pause the game to snap the lights on
she looked at Mouse
and thought
Mouse knew
Mouse understood

Was it possible?
Maybe not
But Mouse knew
and for once
she was glad
For once
it was
OK

The voice called again
This time she could make out the name
Mouse
A sweet name
Even sweeter in that voice

'Mouse.'

A quick lick on her nose and Mouse ran off
leaving the squeaky ball
almost like a
promise

Rubber Gloves

The spray
All purpose
That smelled like apples
Open windows
A breeze
Carrying smells she'd forgotten
Fresh cut grass
Flowers
Sounds
Buzzing and chirping
Distant laughter

Her muscles
Ached
Every step
Sent pain
Springing from
Deep inside
She was sure her legs were
Screaming
Her arms refused to move
She felt
Great

Everything
Was clean
Was Fresh
Everything smelled
Like apples

Mouse Had Come Back

Stomping over forget-me-nots
Running through the grass
Paws scooping up the early morning
Dew drops
Tongue out
Ears flapping like wings

Beth opened the window
'Good morning!'
A bark
'Welcome back!'

Mouse snatched up the toy from where
It had been waiting
The little pink squeaky ball
And brought it to Beth's
Open palm

She gave the dog a friendly pat on the head
A scratch behind one perked ear
The sun
Newly risen
Beaming down
Warming fur and skin
Brightening the day

She threw the ball
And they settled in to

A steady rhythm
Throw
Retrieve
Throw
Retrieve
The ball got slippier
With drool and dew
Mouse's tail moved faster
As paws pounded
Big body bounding
Back and forth

She threw the ball
Harder
Further than usual
It rolled in between trees
And as Mouse turned
And bounced through the garden
The ball
Came flying back

Family

They say people
Look like their dogs
Or that dogs
Look like their people

She didn't look like Mouse
And Mouse didn't look like her
But it was clear
That they belonged to each other
They shared a nature
A tenderness
A soft confidence
They radiated safety
They were warm

They were their own
Family
Small
But whole
And even before learning this new person's name
Even before either of them uttered
A
Single
Word
She couldn't help but feel
A shy spark of hope
That they might have room
In their world
For just one more

Through the Trees

Came a flash of pink
And a voice
Sunny and covered in sleep
'There you are!'
Mouse ran for the ball
Dropping it in Beth's hand
And settled down beneath the window
Watching the
Girl in pink
Tip her way through the garden
Taking care
Not to step on the forget-me-nots

'Mouse, what are you up to?'
She looked up at Beth
Who was suddenly so aware of her mismatched
Pyjamas
Her morning breath
Her unbrushed hair

She looked at this new person
In her pink sundress
Hugging her
Floating around her
Her eyes were heavy with sleep
She held a hand over them
Not ready for the morning sun
She grimaced
A nose wrinkle

'I'm so sorry, has Mouse been bothering you?
Oh my gosh it's so early!'
The voice was even kinder
Up close
The words landed
Like a reassuring hand
Making it hard to care about the pjs
She didn't know what to say
Or how to act
But she needed this new person to stay
That
She knew for sure

'Um … no, no not at all
We were just – playing.'
She cringed internally
The girl laughed
'Yeah that sounds like my Mouse all right.
I'm Alice.
We live just across the street
Through the trees.'
Beth tried to reply
But it had been a while
Since she'd met someone
New
And even longer
Since she'd met someone
She wanted to know
So badly
So quickly

'I'm Beth.'

Alice smiled
And Beth's heart fluttered
Just a little
And she thought
She saw Alice
Blush

'Well, I need to get to work
Come on buddy, let's get you home.'
Mouse whined
And plucked the ball from the ground
Turning to give it back to Beth

'Actually –'
She hadn't planned it
It just came out
Surprising all three
And now
There was no going back

'Um
If you want
If it's
OK
Maybe
Um
Mouse is more than welcome to
Stay

Here
With
Um
Me'
Her cheeks were on fire
'We could keep each other
Company
While you're at work ...'
She wanted to smack her forehead
To shut the window
And the curtains
And dive beneath the blankets
And stay there
Stupid
So
So
Stupid

'That would be great, actually.'
Alice smiled
'Are you sure it wouldn't be too much hassle?'

Surprise took over Beth's face
It must have shown because
Alice's smile got bigger
Her surprise seeped into her voice
She could see it all on Alice's face
Something like
Like
Like a

Longing
A wish
A hint
That maybe she
Was lonely
too
'No, no not at all
We have fun together
Right Mouse?'
A tail wag
Always a tail wag

Alice moved closer
Onto the step of the porch
'I finish work at 4, is that OK?'
'Yeah, yeah that's perfect.'
'Cool.'
'Cool.'
'OK.'
They laughed
'See you later then.'
'See you.'

Mouse

Followed her around all day
She talked and talked
Telling Mouse
Everything
When Mouse fell asleep
Head on her lap
She ran her finger over the silky fur
And read
And everything felt different
She felt like the day
Meant something
More
Bigger
Better

Mouse Saw Her First

Bang bang bang
A very excited tail on the wall
Alice

Beth opened the door
'Hey.'
'Hey.'
Mouse ran out
Straight to Alice
Licking her knees
Until she bent down
And got full slobber attack to the face

She looked up at Beth
Still standing just inside the door

'Thank you, so much! I really appreciate you
Looking after Mouse.'

'My pleasure.'

She tried to fill the two words with enough sincerity
To make her question
Seem OK

'I could – if you want –
Hang out with Mouse tomorrow too.'

'Really?'

Alice's face lit up
So vividly that it had
To mean more
But Beth blew that thought away

Foolish

'That would be amazing!
Is it cool if we come over around 8am?'

'Perfect'

And they left
And she was alone
Knowing that this time
It wasn't for long

It Had Been Five Days

Of 8am drop off in the garden
She always looked forward to
Alice's dresses
The way she looked
Like a princess coming through the trees
Mouse always bounded over
Straight into the house
And conked out on the sofa
And they used small talk
To disguise
How happy they were to see each other

'Tomorrow is Saturday.'
Alice said it like it meant more
Than just the fact
'I don't work on Saturdays.'
Oh
'Oh.'
So she wouldn't see her
Or Mouse
She would be alone
All day
'OK ...'
She nodded
Trying to end the conversation
To glide back to small talk
'But –'
Alice blurted
'I was wondering if maybe ... you would want to ...

Hang out?
With … me?
And Mouse
Of course.'
It was a ramble
Fast and filling a silence
That didn't exist
The yes had left Beth's lips
Before she'd spent a second considering it
'I would love to … is here OK?'
A smile so full of relief
'Here is perfect.'

Paper People

After months
And
Weeks and
Days
With only
Paper people
With paper lives and
Paper hearts and faces that existed
Only on the pages and
In her head
Safe in the silence
People she could imagine and change
And put back on the shelf
People she could talk to but get nothing back
Silent tiny people with silent lives and silent minds
People with ink blood and alphabet veins
Here she was
A Person
Unpredictable
Unexpected
Tangible
She moved and changed the world around her
She smelled of a sweet perfume
She was real and there and
A Person and
Oh
What a person

Changes

She would have to adjust the plan

The Plan

She would have to make
Changes

But the plan
The Plan
Hadn't changed

The Plan
Had never
changed

The Plan worked
Every day
It had been months of
The Plan
Every day
And maybe things weren't better
But things weren't worse
And for her
For now
that was
enough

It had been enough when she'd made the plan
It had been enough when it was all
She had

But now
She had more
She hoped

Yes
She thought
With a defiant nod to no one
The plan will have to change

Day One

She hadn't slept
Nerves
Or butterflies
Or a mix of the two
Kept her fidgeting
All Night Long

But when the sun came up
It scratched out almost all of her worry

It was warm
Bright
Daisies covered the garden

The grass was unruly

She hoped they wouldn't notice

It was 10am
The morning had gone as
Mornings go
But this was where it
Changed

In two hours
They would be here
It wouldn't be just
Her
It would be them

The Door

The door had been opened
Once a week
The door was opened
The nice man
With the thick beard
And thin hair
Who never asked questions
Carried in the boxes
Of pasta and milk and shower gel
And everything
Just one person needs
To get by

One Step

The door had been opened
But she hadn't stepped beyond
The door frame
In six months

She stood with her toes just
At the edge
Of the sunshine

She held out a hand
Felt warmth on her fingers
The slightest breeze

One step
Warm wood beneath her bare feet
That breeze
Sweeping over her arms
One step

A deep breath
New air
Sweeping the dust from her bones
From the very bottom of her lungs
Old skin cells blew away
Carried away
Leaving her fresh

The sun prickled her shoulders

Just a little
Just enough
To say
Welcome back

One step

One step

Picnic

A blanket
Soft and thick
Two cushions
Thick and only a little lumpy
Two mugs
Ready for tea
A plate
Covered with cookies
So many types
That one
Had to be the right one
A green bowl
Full of dog treats
Little white bones
That smelled of chicken
And dog breath
That had made the delivery man
With the beard
Raise an intrigued eyebrow
And smile a little more than usual
She thought maybe he could sense her jitters
Her excited nerves
And was wishing her the best

Arrival

Mouse arrived first
That pink tongue drooped to one side
Of an open mouth
That could only be
A puppish smile

'Hey, buddy.'
She knew she needed to take that one step again
She knew she could
She just had to
Do it

'Come on.'
She wiggled her toes
Come on
She willed her feet to move
Come
On

Everything was heavy

And there was Alice
The sun hit her hair and turned it to gold
Her sun-dress
Blue today
Swished around her knees
Her cheeks were bright and her eyes were locked
Right on Beth's

'Mouse.'

It was a tiny murmur
Almost a whimper
That betrayed the fear
The uncertainty
But it was enough
She felt that scraggy head bump her palm
The smooth tongue give a reassuring swipe
Across her thumb
And they moved together
Just one step
And it was enough

The Day it Went Away

It was hot outside
The last seconds of the walk to work
Were uphill
A small, steep hill
At the top there was safety and
Air
At the bottom there was panic and
Breathlessness
And here
There was a hill
A small steep hill
A hill that brought her to one of only two sanctuaries she had
left
But took oxygen in return
She was relatively fit
She was strong
She could take a hill
A small hill
A steep hill
She knew
She knew
It was just a hill
Ten
Seconds
And she would be in the cool mahogany room
Surrounded by words and friends and the smell of paper in
the
Air
Air

She wondered
For the millionth time
If it was possible for a body to forget how to breathe
To get so distracted by fear and heat and sweat and eyes
That lungs just don't work
Air doesn't come in
Carbon dioxide doesn't come out
Pressure builds and everything hurts and hurts and
Stops
She doubted it was possible but
She felt like it was possible
Probable
Even
She took a deep breath
As deep as the lump in her throat and knot in her chest would allow

Crocodile Cookies

Alice had plopped herself down onto the blanket
Popped a biscuit into her mouth
(a chocolate covered cookie shaped like a crocodile)
Smiled right at Beth
and said
'My favourite!'

Beth could have sworn her heart
twirled
In her chest

Until the Sun Set

They sat
They drank too much tea
They ate all of the biscuits
They laughed
Alice never mentioned Beth's back
pressed heavily against the doorframe
her hand that stayed inside
fingers tapping a steady
light beat on the wooden floor of the kitchen
Alice saw
Beth knew
She waited for the familiar surge of humiliation
for the magnetic pull of
beneath the blankets
But all she could imagine
all that came to mind
was what it would be like to be
beneath the blankets
with Alice
With their hands entangled
and their warm breath filling the space
and it was good
and everything
was good
And Mouse ran around the garden
a happy trot that made them giggle
bringing twigs and leaves to show off
with a smug, proud look on that goofy face
and everything
was
so
good

After

When the air had started to prickle
and goosebumps stood
they said goodnight
reluctant
Slow
like wading through warm water
they smiled at each other
neither was entirely sure
how the hours had passed
what they had talked about
what they had done
In their minds the day was a pink, glowy memory
that meant everything and nothing and everything in between
It was the start of something that felt infinite
something that didn't feel new
But comfortable
But right
Something that fit

That Night

The blankets welcomed her
She wrapped herself up tight
the evening chill sitting in her bones
sending little shivery waves up to her skin
as a physical
undeniable
reminder
that it was real
that she had done it
that she wasn't alone any more

Alice

A dry patch between her eyebrows
Soft peach fuzz on her lip
Tiny pink marks dotted
      Here
          And
              There
A shiny white scar on her cheek
Opalescent when she looked up
A gentle pearly dip
Short hair
Swooping over her forehead
Too dark to be blond
Too light to be brown
Full of humidity and summer sweat
Freckles, orange on blush
A sweet little chin
A bump that danced when she laughed
Made faces when she frowned
Blue eyes
An in between, everyday blue
A blue that didn't sparkle
A blue you couldn't dive into
A blue that didn't matter
Her eyes were kind
They crinkled
They closed when her smile demanded all of the attention
When her little tongue poked out from between her teeth
Like every smile
Could be a laugh

Could be more
With her
Everything went on
There was always more
There was no destination
No end
There was always more
It could get bigger
It could get better
Everything was full of more and more and more
Everything was moving
Nothing stayed still
Nothing hid
Nothing ran
Everything
Just
Was
With her

The Day It Went Away II

She had reached the door of the bookshop
The creaky wooden door
With glass windows
So covered in posters
And signs
That it was impossible to see through

She opened the door
Ready to leave the heat
Ready for the cool
Wooden room
Ready to sit
And breathe
And feel OK

She stepped in
Waited for the cool air to sweep over her sticky skin
But it never came

A Gift

Alice had a different smile
It turned up on one side
Betraying an almost cocky pride

'I brought you something!'

Beth beamed
Blushing at the fuss
Swept up in the flare
In the moment

Alice's hand disappeared into the bag
Resurfacing
Triumphantly
With a
Book

A book of fairytales
A book with a glittering cover
A rich purple ribbon
Elaborate
Twirling letters
And a tiny
Blue price sticker
That sent Beth's brown eyes
Glowing green

Jealousy

Alice
After a day
Of work
Of people
Of conversation
Alice
In the bookshop
Pushing the door
Hearing the little bell
The tinkle
That had greeted Beth
Every
Day
Alice
Surrounded by the smell of paper
And ink
Tiptoeing around stacks
Running her fingers over spines
Her eyes over stories
Alice
Surrounded by the silence of the
Small
Wooden
Sanctuary
That used to be
Hers

Hers

The bookshop was the same in her head
It looked the same
Smelled the same
Meant the same
But it had moved on
Without her
The space she had left
Had been filled
Filled with someone
Who was a
Someone
A person
A person Alice sees
A person who sees Alice
A person Alice talks to
Knows
She didn't know why it hurt
If anything
It was good
But it felt
Like the last
The end
The hand drop
The end of the train platform
The moment the plane is lost to the clouds
She tried to shake it away
She had left it

She knew that
But now
She felt that
It had left her
And it hurt all over again

Alice's smile had dropped
Sunk
Lower and lower
Until she looked pained
Confused
Warily apologetic

The words
'You don't like it.'
Slipped from her lips
Like velvet
Rubbing the wrong way
Sending uneasy shivers across skin
Making fingers curl inwards

Beth loved it
Beth loved it desperately
Loved it with a hunger
That roared and rampaged inside of her
Banging against the jealousy
But sliding to the ground
Defeated

She missed her life for the first time
She missed the bookshop for the thousandth

She was jealous
Of Alice for her life
For her days
For her stories
Written on a fresh page every damn day

Of the bookshop
For going on without her
For seeing change
Filling up with different footsteps
Hearing new voices

Of the world
The world beyond her world
For Alice
For having her too
For being able to show her new things
Give her new things
For change

She tried to say it all
She tried to say that
She was sorry
That she was jealous
Jealous
Jealous
Jealous
That she was stuck
That she was glue
That she was a trap
That she wanted to be more

That she wanted to be good enough
That she wanted to be enough
But words didn't fit and Alice
Alice
Wouldn't understand
Couldn't
Possibly
And with all of it filling her up
Weighing her down
She just said
'Please go.'

Out

She slept all night with Alice on her eyelids
Afraid to wake and see her
Confused and hurt
So she ignored the doorbell
Once
Twice
For a single second
She thought of
Pretending she was out
Then she rolled over
Laughed viciously at herself
And went back to sleep

Doorbell

Every day the doorbell rang
Three days
Under the covers
Muttering
That this was the
Right thing to do
The fair thing

Alice would realise soon
Alice would do the smart thing
Alice would give up

Four Days

The doorbell rang
And rang
And rang
Morning
Midday
Evening
It rang with patience
It didn't demand an answer
It was just a reminder
That when she was ready
It would still ring

Day Five

She answered the door
Waited for the anger
For the questions
But Alice
Of course
Alice
Just smiled
Like it hadn't been days
Like nothing had happened
And said
'Do you want to talk about it?'
Beth's shields flew up
'You don't understand.'

'No.'

She knew
Of course
She knew
But the confirmation
That a part of her was
Too different
Stung

'But I'd like to try.'

Building the Fort

The deck was becoming
Less scary
But her back was always
Glued to the doorframe

No matter how badly she wanted to move
To scooch closer
She
Just
Couldn't
Her limbs would only listen
To the scared part of her brain
The part that screamed loudest
The part that made the rules
The part that always won

Alice saw
The way she always did

Mouse arrived first
Carrying a tote bag
Now with added drool
She took the bag and peeked in
And saw pink
Before she could figure out what she was looking at
A happy chirp from the door
Said
'I have an idea!'

And there Alice was
Behind a massive
Overflowing box
Sheets and pillows and long strings
Of lights
Alice
And her ideas

Pink Sheets

Draped from the window
To the edge of the deck
Like sails on a boat
Bobbing along
Always ready to take them back
To their little island

Fairy lights hung in swoops
Pillows covered the walls
And the floor
The sun streaming through the sheet
Made the little fort
Glow like a constant sunset

Alice Had to Pee

'Um.'
'I can just run over to my house, it's OK!'
Why did she do that?
How was she so understanding of something
She didn't know
Something they never mentioned?
She stood up
Smoothing her skirt
It was raining
'No – no no no.'
Alice's eyebrows shot up
A little worry
A little confusion
'The bathroom is through the kitchen and to the left.'
It was a shaky murmur
Alice smiled and darted to the door
'Oh thank goodness!'
She sang
Beth listened to Alice
Crashing through the kitchen
She heard her
Ooph
As she banged into the table
Clumsy in her rush
In her house
Beth's house
Beth smiled
A quiet

Revelation
A realisation
That she felt
Proud
Of herself
And that
It felt
So good

When Alice Came Back

Her body looser
A dopey smile on her face
She flopped onto the blankets and said
'Your house is perfect,
It feels like
You.'

What did that mean?
It felt like her?
Her pride wavered

She looked at Alice
Caught her gazing at her
She didn't look away
No hint of embarrassment
At being caught
She just kept looking at her
Looking at Beth
Making easy eye contact
Even with the angry parts of her mind
Insisting that she was broken
That she was a burden
Even with it yelling from the inside
The way Alice looked at her
Pushed it back
Pushed it
Squashed it
Made it cower

Hide
The way Alice looked at her
Told her
And almost
Made her believe
That she was anything
But broken

Until the Sun Set II

As the days went by
and picnics grew more

        and more

        elaborate

and they learned each other
through snacks and teas and flowers
books and memories
through where a smile started and a laugh died out
Alice liked pink
she loved her job
loved teaching
Beth liked green
and she had loved her job too
The jealousy had made way for relief
she had regained something
something had come back to her
Every day spent with
this girl and this dog
brought something
added something
new things
old things
things she forgot
things she missed
everything grew
her life grew
her world stayed the same
this small house
these old walls
but everything got bigger

The Next Day

Alice wore green
And Beth
Felt
An
Extra
Flicker
Of
Hope

Hands

Her hand
Was curves
Curves
Bumps
Tiny dips and hills that
Fit themselves into hers

It was warm
Soft
She felt each line that ran through her skin
Each little rough patch where she put her worries
The ragged bits of skin around her fingernails
The barely there hairs above her knuckles
A small scrape below her thumb

It was shape
It was slopes
It was warm
A little clammy with summer
It shook just the tiniest amount
But it didn't go
Anywhere

It was heavy
Sturdy
Sure
It was there
It was

Definitely
There

It held her smaller hand with a confident care
With a strong, sweet
I've been waiting for this
I've been looking for this
This is everything
Everything is this

The air around their interlaced fingers was muggy
Heavy with nerves
with all of the times they'd imagined
This
Exact
Moment

Her hand wasn't cold
It wasn't smooth and hard
Not like glass
When they untangled her fingers hadn't left a smudge
But her fingerprints were there
On Alice's skin
And Alice's were on hers
Lightly printed where they had touched
Where they had held
Hands

Touch

She stood in front of the mirror
Towel wrapped tight around her middle
The sunlight hitting the ground warmed her feet
As she stared into her own eyes
And saw Alice

Alice was soft
She was shapes
She took up space
Proudly and
Confidently
She stood firm on the ground
She had a place
She was part of something
She existed and she knew it and she held onto her space
In the world with a determination
That glistened in her eyes
And added strength to her body
Made her tall and strong and solid
She was a person
She was Alice

The girl in the mirror wasn't Alice
She was her
Just her
Her shapes were smaller
Less sure
More apologetic

Her whole body looked
Apologetic
Sorry for taking up space
Closed in
Trying to be as small as possible
Trying to stay
Out of the way

She folded the towel over the radiator
Looked at her toes in the glass
And worked
Her way
Up
She looked at every inch the mirror could show her
Skin, bones, muscles, veins, lumps, bumps, scratches,
scars, spots, hairs, freckles
All of it
All of her
Her soft belly
Her wibbly arms
Her hairy legs

She wondered if Alice ever had hairy legs
She wondered if Alice's skin was soft and smooth or
dented and dimpled
If her thighs rubbed against each other until they were
warm and red and itchy
If her pants dug angry marks into her belly
If her cheeks flared and her breath escaped her

All of these things she hated
About her own
Timid, shaky body
All of these things
She tried so hard to
Ignore
To forget
To hide

All of these things
On Alice
Were perfect
All of these things
Were more of Alice
More of her to know
To experience
To drink in
To touch
To Feel

A blush blossomed and she shook the thought away
The moment their hands had touched ran on repeat
through her mind
She put a hand on her stomach
That hand
The hand that had felt Alice's
She imagined it was Alice's hand
A secure, warm weight
Would she worry?
Would she panic?

Would she push her hand away?

Or would it all be worth it
To be touched
By her?

Nothing

It isn't sadness
Not really
It's a barrier
It's every bit of you
Being locked up
Kept from each other
You become a prison
All locked up
You are there
But you're disjointed
There's nothing happening
Not really
Nothing bad
Not really
Nothing good
Just nothing
And
It hurts to be nothing
It hurts to not hurt
To have nothing
Not even sadness
Not even pain
Not even tears
Or anger
So you create it
You create pain
You slice and pinch and punch
Because something
Anything
Is better than nothing
It has to be

Guilt

She looked at her hand
The faded freckles and jagged nail beds
Nails bitten so low it looked
almost as painful
as it felt

She couldn't remember biting them
She knew it was a habit
that popped its head up
When panic loomed
But she had no real idea of when she had done it
Ripped them off
Left bright red skin visible
Skin that was used to having a shield

She'd pulled at her cuticles
tore them from where they lay and
as she stared at them now she couldn't stop
imagining
her nail
falling right
out
leaving her with unprotected little stumps for fingers
red and raw and exposed
She shivered at the idea
Tried to push it away
Stomp it out
but it rolled around her head so fast she couldn't catch it
Her stomach turned

She raised a fist and smacked her forehead until
blinding pain made the thought
made any thought
impossible.

She was numb
For a while
She liked being numb
It was a break
An escape
She thought of nothing
Focused on the searing pain in her head
the heat on her temple
The throbbing just below her skin
Nothing else existed
Nothing else mattered
And she could breathe
For a
minute

But the fog clears fast
Thoughts and feelings flood back and try their
damn hardest to make up for lost moments
A tiny fleck of fear yelled that she could really hurt herself
A hint of stubbornness muttered that she was hers to hurt

This always happened
The same thoughts in the same order
The nice part of her brain trying to force regret
The rest laughing indignantly

But this time
There was something new
A new picture flickering in
the space between

Her Face
Alice
Mouse's ears
Alice's hands
Her eyes
Always worried
But always hopeful
Always watching her
Seeing her

They cared
She knew it
She couldn't deny it

and she couldn't stand it

Guilt ripped through her middle
It hurt
So
Much
More
Than the bruise blooming on her head
Than the dull ache in her knuckles
Than her ravaged fingernails

She felt herself double over
Her eyes glaze with tears
She wanted to slap herself
Sharply
Right across
Her too-hot cheek
But their faces were in her head
Their eyes were seeing the dried blood on her fingers
The bruise
The pain

She was hers to hurt
She was hers
To hurt
She was
Hers
To
Hurt

But they
weren't

A Yellow Envelope

It arrived early in the morning
Falling to the floor with a swish
A quiet intruder
Lying in wait
To be picked up
Turned over and over
To have fingers swept across the
Tiny letters
Tracing the familiar handwriting

She knew what it was
She knew what it would say
Happy Birthday
The yearly reminder that
She mattered
But she wasn't ready
To matter
So she left the words
the wishes
Sealed inside the card
And she pushed them to the
Back of a drawer and
The back of her mind

The Next Morning Brought Blood

soaked through layers
all the way down

Strip the bed
undress
shower
ugly underwear
thick pants
laundry
nothing
nothing
nothing

The blood made everything bigger

Cramps

A fist plunged into her abdomen
Twisting
Squeezing
Digging
Nails scraping, tearing her insides
Blood on pyjama pants
Blood soaked underwear
Blood decorating her thighs
Like gory Rorschach tests
Unfortunate tattoos
Flowers pressed between muscles
Blood on the bed sheets
Like poppies
Blood
Everywhere
Blood on her fingers
Blood in the toilet
Just blood and mess and blankets and
CRAMPS
Five days
Five full days
Five days
Full
Of so many
Missed months
Months and months
Of a different pain
A deeper

Empty
Bloodless
Ache
Five
Days
Of
C R A M P S
And
CRAMPS
And
Cramps

Alice Brought Options

Thick cotton pads
With sticky wings and
A chemical scent
Tampons in neon
plastic tubes
Covered in flowers
She brought pills
Capsules
Hot water bottles
Chocolate
She brought comfort
She brought a reminder
That this was good
And that it
Would all
Be over
Soon

Reason

Alice took her hand
As soft as ever
Running her fingers over the battered knuckles
As if performing a spell

'I can't be
your reason.'

She was right
They both knew
She was right

She looked at Alice
Saw how much she wanted
To help
To hold her together
Her voice crackled
'You're my only reason.'
It sounded like an apology
She felt like one big
Apology

'I don't have any other
reason.'

She saw tears in Alice's eyes and the knowledge that
They were her doing made her fists
Tighten

Alice noticed
Alice always noticed

She shook her head
'You're reason enough.'
Alice's voice was kind
But it shook
It had a tinge
Of something like anger
A tiredness
A hint of desperation
She wrapped her hands around Beth's balled up fist
Rubbing gentle circles into the stiff fingers
Until they loosened
Until they forgot to be
so angry
Until all they felt was her
'I'm here
I'm with you
And I will tell you
And tell you
Until I'm blue in the face
How strong you are
How worthy you are
Until you listen
Until you're ready
To accept it
Until you're ready
To lift your fists back up
And fight
Your way out
I'll keep telling you

You're enough.'

Breakfast

Alice's eyes were puffy in the mornings
Her cheeks were pink circles
Her lips red from yawning
She always managed to get a little toothpaste
In the corner of her mouth
And her eyebrows were
always
Adorably unruly
Laces still untied as she floated to Beth

Mouse was always sleepy too
Leaden paws
Fur sticking out in every direction
But the intended one
Dropping heavily
immediately
in the pillow fort
snoring
It had been weeks of this
of mornings

Alice and Mouse and Beth
She was always ready
Standing at the door
Waiting
Mouse would sleep
Beth would hand Alice a steaming coffee
In a mug almost as big as her head

Alice would smile sleepily
Sip with her eyes closed
Throw back her head
Sigh
Then meet Beth's eyes and
Beth watched her allow herself
To wake up
Beth liked it that she was always the first thing
Alice really saw
In the mornings
Beth went about her mornings
imagining Alice
Stumbling from the bed to
The bathroom to
The wardrobe
Tripping over clothes and books and dog toys
Imagining Mouse
Gobbling down breakfast without even peeking
And they would come
Across the street
Through the trees
To her
And she would be so wide awake
So sunny
The kitchen would smell so good
Like coffee and soap and baking
She would hand over the bucket of coffee
And Alice would finally wake up
And look at her
And smile

And she would smile back
Still shy
Still quiet
But with a new lightness
She had started baking
Wrapping snacks in neat little packages
Slipping them into Alice's bag
While she nursed her coffee
Content little murmurs escaping the mug
They never spoke
In the mornings
But they both let out
A little squeal once the door was closed
And then the day could begin

Lunch

Lunch time was Beth and Mouse
Mouse's head would pop out of the pillow fort
Droopy eyes
Tail swishing in a dopey rhythm
Nose sniffing, twitching a little dance
Dragging that big, happy body to where
Beth sat
With a book
Plopping a fluffy head on Beth's knee
Blinking
Yawning
Snuggling into her lap
Fur tickling Beth's wrist
As her eyes dashed to the end of the page
Laughing to herself
Mouse followed her to the kitchen
Always at her feet
Always looking at her, ears perked
As she talked about the book
The story
The characters
The suspense
The romance
They shared a sandwich
Mouse liked the crusts
Beth didn't
Beth drank tea
Mouse drank milk

Slurping noisily
Beth talked the entire time
She talked so much
That the house filled with words
Not important words
Words that blew right out of the open windows
But words that made silence feel OK
When it visited
Made it feel temporary
Friendly
And Mouse always listened
To every word
Tail wagging when Beth was excited
Low whines when she was moved
Always there

Dinner

Dinner had been forgotten
So many times
Overshadowed by the sunset
And the conversation

Until Alice
Craving spring rolls
Brought bags and boxes
And chopsticks
And they sat in the fort
Protected by blankets
Passing small cardboard containers
Back and forth
Giggling as they struggled with their chopsticks
Dropping noodles and sauce
All over the day

Dinner became Alice's
She would bring boxes
Or bags
Or canvas totes full of vegetables
From the market beside the bookshop
That Beth used to pass
But never braved
They pored over recipe books together
Learning their tastes
Learning what they liked
Beth grew more confident

More comfortable
The kitchen became another part of their world
Mouse in the garden
Chasing the scents
Beth and Alice
Watching
Laughing
Burning and boiling and grilling and eating
Sometimes ordering pizza
Sometimes worrying about garlic breath
Or spinach between their teeth
Always lying in the pillow fort
With full, warm bellies
While nice Mouse licked plates clean

Dancing

Alice had brought a song
She carried it to Beth
Humming it to herself all the way home
Just in case it left her
Before she could share it

She didn't say hello
Just took Beth's hands
Pulling her close
The September wind blew the fairy lights
Making them dance around them like stars
Turning their world into
A galaxy
Alice wrapped an arm around Beth's waist
Concentrating so hard
That her lips formed a little tulip pout
And a little line appeared between her eyebrows
Beth started to say her name
Confused and smitten
But Alice just caught her eye
And gave a little smile
Beth was tracing shapes on her back
With one thumb
Staring at that little line between those messy eyebrows
Alice started to hum
Her voice was uneven and shaky
But it sent warmth all the way to Beth's bones
She hummed the whole song

She couldn't remember the words
But the words didn't matter
This wasn't about words
This was about them
This was about her
She held her
This girl
This Girl
And she hummed and
And Beth listened
And watched
And she knew
That Alice could feel what she felt
And the knowledge made a home in her
And she swore
A silent
Private promise
That she would give this
Right back
To Alice
She wanted this for her
She wanted her to feel this
Even just for one
Moment
This lightness
Or heaviness
Or maybe just a total lack of
Everything
She felt everything and nothing
She felt like she was everywhere and nowhere

Like they had stumbled into
The space between
everything
She knew what this feeling was
She knew what it was and who it was for
And it came with the fluffiest, pinkest glow
That sat in her chest
And made her feel
Like this is how people should feel
She knew what this was
She knew

She Thought

That even if this feeling
Lived
And stayed
And died
In her
In her chest
That was OK
Because nothing else had made her feel
This
No one else
Had made her feel this
And
This
Was perfect
This was
What life was about
And for this
Alice
Deserved the world
Alice deserved the whole galaxy
And every star
And she looked at her
And Alice was looking right back
Taking her all in
She wasn't smiling
But she looked
How Beth felt

Reading

Sometimes Alice brought books
They smelled like the bookshop
And Alice's perfume

Sometimes Beth would read the books
Her voice filling the fort
With stories
Alice would kick her shoes from her tired feet
Slowly run her hands over her full belly
And watch as Beth got lost
As she relaxed
Giving characters voices
And dramatic pauses
And sound effects
Too lost to look down
And notice the eyes
Taking in every bit of her they could get
Cherishing her
Every moment with everything she was

Touch II

It was late
She wasn't sure how late
But sleep wasn't coming
And the thoughts weren't going
Anywhere

It had been hours
since Alice and Mouse
Had left
Sleepily making the short trip
Through the trees

But when she closed the door
Alice was still there
She saw her everywhere
They brushed their teeth together
Alice's arms wrapped around her
So tight she swore
She could almost
Feel them
Feel her hand
Sneak under her shirt
Across her stomach
Nails
Grazing
Just enough
To send tingles
Buzzing through her
She tried to shake it away

But the Alice whose hungry eyes watched
Her as she undressed
Only flickered the tiniest bit
And went
Nowhere
She slipped under the covers
And closed her eyes
Willing sleep to come
But Alice was beside her
Hair tickling her dark skin
Her shoulder
Her stomach
Her thighs
Her eyes flew open
She couldn't tell
If the heat in her cheeks
Was a blush
Or a flush
Or what the squiggles in her tummy
Were trying to tell her
She tried to sleep
But Alice's
Hands were on her
Alice's chest was pressed against her back
Her fingers trailing
Down her side
She tossed and turned and stared at the ceiling
Wishing
She could stop
Wishing
She could want to stop

But she couldn't
She never wanted the touching to stop
She wanted more
She wanted
So much more
She wanted
It all
She wanted everything
With Alice
She thought of Alice
At home
In her bed
She imagined silky pink sheets
Gliding like water over her skin
Alice's eyes closed
Mouth open
Moans escaping her lips
She pictured it
And it took over
She ran her hand down her stomach
Remembering Alice's fingers on hers
Imagining
What they could do
Her fingers slipped beneath her
Waistband
A little gasp escaped her
And the Alice beside her
Watched
Eyes wide
Taking it all in

Tongue darting along her lower lip
Little gasps
Making tickles buzz across Beth's skin
As she imagined hands
In her hair
On her neck
Dipping down
Fingers
Telling stories
In delicate script
In scrawling letters
Tongues
Tasting everything
Savouring
Everything
She felt her body move
In ways she didn't know it could
She felt
Good
She felt
Right
She felt whole
She felt everything falling into place
Clicking into place
Coming together
She wanted everything
And she wanted it with her

October

Leaves and conkers and apples

Soft brown leather
Laced up
Around Alice's feet
Dancing, clumsily
In the rain of red
                    Orange
                            Yellow
                                    Gold

She watched
The little world they had added
Stitched onto the very edge of her own
Another part of the patchwork
Right outside her door
On the worn
                    Weathered
                                    Wood
A bridge between them

Which had been nothing
For
            So
                    Long
Empty but for
Dirty shoes
Crumbled coal
Splintered wood

Now
It had life
It was a home
To two girls
And a dog

Three Together

In the world between their worlds
Where it was
Different
Where it was
Good

Hallowe'en

The doorbell wouldn't stop
Devils and ghosts and witches
Beth hid from it all
From the feet
Trudging through the garden
She jumped with every ring
Waited for voices to fade
Alice passed out sugar
Until it ran out
Then they turned off the lights
And ignored the world

November

Twinkle lights and lumpy cushions
Bit
By
Bit
Every week a new addition to the little land
A new tea to try
A new book to flick through
A new squeaky ball to chase
Each week another scarf
Another layer
Until hats were woolly
And gloves were too thick
To turn pages
And warm tea turned cold
So fast
And whiskers shimmered with ice
And tiny teeth chattered

The pumpkins turned to mulch
The ground became too hard to
Hide prized treats in and
Every silence was full of foggy speech bubbles

Their world
That had warmed and comforted
Was ready for sleep

And her own little
Private
World
The world that held everything
She couldn't hold inside
The World of One
Was ready
To welcome
Two more

Taking Down the Fort

The cold had infiltrated the fort
The wind whipped through the sails
Disrupting the little life
Within the linen walls
Forcing the crew
To land

The Lights Went First

Like plucking stars
From the sky
Leaving it dark
Like winter mornings
The walls
The ceiling
Torn down
Falling like sand
Caught in the wind
They worked together
Taking it all down
Piece by piece
Putting everything back in the box
Both secretly hoping
They would be opening it again
Together
When the sun came back
But until then
They had logs in the fireplace
Fuzzy socks on the radiator
And interlaced fingers
And so
Together
They went inside

Alice Had a Cold

Beth had opened the door
Cradling the usual morning coffee
And found a nose like a cherry
Pink chapped lips
And eyes watering with self pity
She looked at Alice
At strong, beautiful Alice
Standing at her door
Snowflakes in her hair
Boots on her feet
And pyjamas on her shivery body
They were pink
Covered in bunnies
With little pompoms for tails
And dorky smiles on their faces
Her hair stood up at all angles
Her cheeks glowed
And she clutched a pair of slippers
More bunnies
More pompoms

Beth let out a sympathetic snort
Put the coffee down and pulled
The pompom laden sniffling mess
Into her arms
And kept her there
All day

The Yellow Envelope II

The yellow envelope
Was on her mind
All night
It got darker earlier
The ground was getting harder
Her breath was starting to turn to tiny
Storm clouds
In front of her face
Taunting her
As the supply
Of crumpled notes
Got smaller
And the numbers
Pouring in the letterbox got bigger
And the yellow envelope
Was still
There
At the bottom of a drawer
She woke early
Shivered her way down the stairs
And pulled the drawer open
Forcefully
Quick enough
That there was no going back
There it was
She picked it up
Held her breath
And tore it open

She didn't know if she was ready
Yet
But she did know
She was ready to find out
The card had a bear holding balloons
And more glitter than it was equipped to hold
It rained on down on the carpet
Tickling her toes
She opened it and smooth
Crisp
New notes
Fell out
And guilt plunged into her tummy
She read the card with tears in her eyes
The reminder that she was loved
That she mattered
And the guilt simmered a little
And she promised the silence
That she would
Let herself
Matter soon
That she
Would let others matter

soon

Inside

Alice
Sitting at the kitchen table
Where Beth drank tea
Climbing up on the old stool
Looking through the shelves
Scouring for conversations
Debates and shared affection
Sitting on the floor in front of the
Fire, warming her hands
Taking milk from the fridge
Cups from the press
Sugar from the shelf
Like she had been
             here
             for ever

Different

The house looked different with Alice in it
It seemed warmer
Softer around the edges
Scruffs seemed suddenly charming
Marks and dents were stories
Squeaks and creaks were the house
Joining the conversation
Laughing alongside
The little
      family

She Had Worried

That merging the outside
With the inside
Flipping the world upside down
Would send her spiralling
Backwards
Would bring her back to the start
Of it all
To the shaking
To the panic
But
Having them there
Her Alice
Her Mouse
Her family
Felt
Nothing
But right
But easy
But
Oh
Of
Course

The New

Alice on the sofa
Mouse in front of the fire
Beth between the two
Right
     Where
         She
            Belonged

It Was a Bad Day

The kind of day that just isn't
       a day
       at all
She knew as she heaved her bones around
That it was
One of Those Days

But
For the first time
It didn't scare her
For the first time
It felt
Temporary
It was
Only
Now
And now
Really
Isn't very long
At all

These Days

It was a bad day
But
It was an Alice day
These days
All days were
Alice Days
Before and after work
Breakfast and dinner
Sunrise and set

She waited at the door
The coffee cup
Burning her hand
Her bones glowing red
Cracking open
Like logs in a fire
Flaming red splinters
She shook
Tried to prise her eyes open
All the way
To look alive
To look alert
To look like someone Alice
Would want to be around

Alice took the cup
Poured the molten caffeine down her throat
Mouse ran past their knees

Straight to the couch
Snuggling under Mount Blanket

Alice looked at her
Scanned her
And she saw
And she knew that she saw
She felt caught
Found out

Alice put a mittened hand on her cheek
'I won't be long.'
A promise

When she returned it was with
Bags and bags of ingredients
It was with new songs
And stories
And logs for the fire
(Beth liked the crackle)
And her hand always found Beth
When she felt she was floating through hours
There was food and stories and songs and crackles
And always a hand
On her back
On her arm
On her fingers
On her cheek
Keeping her there
Keeping her safe
Until she came home

By December

The house felt wrong
Without Alice
Without Mouse
Like being left alone in someone
Else's house
Not uncomfortable
But not comfortable
Either
The house came alive
When all of the pieces came together
Alice had rearranged the kitchen cabinets
Standing on a chair
Chatting about her day
Organising soups and rice and potatoes
Beth threw toys for Mouse
Who bounded through the house
Shaking the foundations
Scaring the furniture
Alice had brought a skillet
A stew pot
A garlic crusher
Slowly she filled the kitchen
So that even when she wasn't there
She was everywhere
She'd turned into quite the cook
'Chef, actually,'
She said
Covered in fake anger and insult

But always spilling smiles
Dog toys filled every corner
Were stuffed under every sofa
Behind every cushion
Everything squeaked
The house had new noises
New languages
But she understood

December

Brought snow and hail and sleet
The fire always roared
Alice had a stash of mittens in the junk drawer
Beth dragged every blanket in the house
To the sofa
Used every spare pillow to make a bed for Mouse

December
Brought them closer
Pressed together
Holding cold hands in warm ones
Nestling under the same blanket

December
Brought the end
A Year
The Year
Her Year

Red for Yellow

Alice arrived with rosy cheeks
And twinkling eyes
Rambling about
Fairy lights
And fir trees
And mistletoe
She brought cards
With little red robins
Wearing hats
Sitting on snowy branches
She scribbled and sang
Building a small pile
Of red envelopes
And Beth wrote one
Filled it with thanks
And added it to the pile
To be sent

The End

She hadn't told Alice
About the year
As the days crept forward
Steadily toward
The day with the fireworks
And the parties
And the promises to be better
To do better
New
To match
New
She felt that
She
Really
Didn't want
Everything
To change

31st December II

7am
It was raining
Heavy
Thuds on the roof
Like listening to too many songs
All at once

9am
The rain had turned to
Hail
Heavy pellets
That stung and smacked

10am
She put on music
To drown out the constant
Smattering
Of icy bullets
She tried to dance
An awkward sway from room
To room
But the noise
The persistent
Overbearing noise
Made her feel like her senses
Were compromised
Like anything could sneak up on
Her

Alone
Surrounded by noise and nothing

11am
Alice didn't knock
Mouse didn't give her the option
Just barged right into the door
Making it swing open
With a violent
Dramatic
Bang
Paws slipped
Slid all the way to the fireplace
Shaking hailstones
All over
The room
That melted
Into tiny lakes

12 noon
They baked
Thunder rolled over the house
Low rumbles that had Mouse
Darting under the table
Peeking out suspiciously
Looking for the culprit
The house smelled of chocolate and coffee

1pm
They danced

Drowning out the thunder with
Cheesy pop
Distracting Mouse
With jazz hands
And air guitars
This time
Beth didn't worry about dampening
Her senses
With Alice around
Her senses
Were always
Alight

2pm
The thunder went from rumbling
To roaring
Mouse had run upstairs
Barraging a big shivering body
In a small safe space
They sat at the foot of the bed
Wrapped in blankets
Fighting thunder with comforting coos
Making up stories about
Rabbits
And squirrels
And brave puppies
Whose bravery and heroism
Could never be broken
Even in the face
Of the loudest thunder
Or the brightest lightning

Until gentle snores rolled like marbles from beneath the
bed
And they tiptoed out

3pm
They pushed the sofa
To the window
Watched the rain flowing down the glass
Making the garden look like
A
Watercolour painting
Every now and then a splash of white
Was added
The lightning lit the room around them
The lights were off
The grey day had made its way in
And their faces were close
Seemingly a little closer with every
Flash of lightning
That found them looking at each other
Blushing in the dark that always followed
Waiting for the next illumination
So they could gaze at each other again

4pm
Alice had fallen asleep
Head on Beth's shoulder
Mouth wide open
Snoring so loud she told stories

5pm
Alice snuggled in to Beth
Nudging her arm up with her face
Until she was nestled in the other girl's armpit
She grinned
Smug and sweet and asleep

Beth was reading
Poring over the words
But lost in another story
A story told in snores
And pages turning
And rain
Hitting a window
Bouncing off flowerpots
Snowflakes and pompoms
Coffee and songs and bunnies
Burned food and dog-eared books and
Pillow forts and worn wood beneath sunburned knees
Sniffles and tissue and the creaking of an old stool
Of fingers running over old hardbacks
The smell of fresh banana bread
With extra chocolate chips
Of mismatched socks
Of cookies
Of Alice
Of her
Of them

Of everything they were

6pm
Alice's head had fallen to Beth's lap
She drooled just the tiniest amount
But Beth didn't mind
Just added another chapter

7pm
Alice woke with a blush
That ran all the way from
Her frizzed hairline
Under her rumpled jumper
She wiped a sleeve wrapped fist
Across her mouth
Yawned and prised the book from
Beth's hands, marked the page
And snuggled down
Taking the sleeping girl's fingers
Stroking her sleepy heat into them
Tucking them
Under the blanket
Tucking her in
Keeping her warm
And safe
And happy
Her eyes fluttered open
And she watched Alice
As she padded around the house
Found thick socks for her cold feet
Fuzzy socks slipping
As she flipped on lamps
Closing curtains

Picking up dog toys
Wandering through this house
That she now seemed to know so well
Listening to Beth describe the dream she'd just had
She opened cupboards
Scooped up ingredients
Slid their favourite cookbook from the shelf
That Beth had set aside for the growing collection
They shared

8pm
Chopped onions
Minced garlic
Sliced aubergine
Plump tomatoes
Oozy mozzarella
Pasta spirals bobbing in bubbling water
Herbs speckling the floor
Around fuzzy socked feet

9pm
Beth woke to
Mouth watering
Garlic infused
Steamy air
She looked to the kitchen
Saw Alice
Leaning over that cookbook
She liked so much
Running a finger down the page

Muttering to herself
Her hair was in a pile on her head
Her apron was hanging off
Tied in a lopsided bow
She had a stain on her leggings
And thick purple socks on her little feet
Beth felt something click inside her
Somewhere in her chest
Here
She was
This girl
In her kitchen
Wearing her socks
Cooking
Making a mess
Flinging open drawers and grabbing pots and pans
Like she's been there forever
Like she would be there forever
Wearing her socks

10pm
Beth had set the table
They moved seamlessly
Wordlessly
Around each other
Singing the song that Beth had picked
Harmonising clumsily
Plates and cutlery
A candle
More candles

Beth blushed when Alice noticed
But she just smiled
And nodded

Mouse had braved the storm
Making the hazardous trek
From the bed to the sofa
Where a bone as long as a wagging tail waited

The food was Alice's best
The garlic bread was charred a little
Just around the sides
But that
Was how Beth liked it
They ate and talked and drank juice from wine glasses
Debating the best pasta shapes
Wearing their pyjamas
Sleep puffed faces
And candlelight
And there were two hours left
And just like last year
She made a decision

11pm
Pasta belly
Is the warmest belly
They had decided
Definitively
They lay on the floor
Of the new pillow fort

A bigger one
With walls made of books
A fleece carpet
And a cotton ceiling
A pillow made a door
Pillows made the furniture
Twinkle lights lit the space
Like fireflies
They had turned all of the lights in the house
Off
And they saw each other
Clearly
Under the tiny starry lights
And they knew they were both thinking
The same thing
And safe in that knowledge they lay down
And they held hands
'Do you have any resolutions?'
'I don't know, do you?'
'I asked first …'
Alice snorted
'OK … I'd like to be braver … I think …Yeah.'
She looked at Beth
Beth took a breath
Trying to fill her words with everything she had
'You are brave.'
'Not all the time. I get scared at work, that I'll mess up
… that someone won't like me
That I'll embarrass myself …'
'But you still go

Every day
That's brave.'
'I just feel scared. A lot.'
Beth broke eye contact
She couldn't imagine Alice being scared
'I never would have guessed,' she murmured
Alice blushed
'I'm never scared when you're around.'
Heat radiated from the hot pink flush of Beth's cheeks
'But I'm …'
It was time
She thought
Time to be honest
Time to say it
She opened her mouth and –
'I know,' Alice said
'I know you're scared
I know you don't leave
And I know why
I get it
I understand
You don't have to explain
Anything to me
Look at what you've done
For me
To me
Look at everything you've given me
You've done so much
Right here
There's plenty out there

And it can wait
Because if you can do this
All of this
If you can make me feel strong
And brave
And
And
Cared for
And happy
Here
Just here
Imagine what you could do
With the whole world
In your hands
It's OK if you aren't ready
The world can wait
For you
You're worth waiting for.'

12 midnight
Fireworks were dazzling in the distance
And they were on the porch
Watching
It was cold
Ice prickled their skin
Beneath layers of blankets
But their hands were warm
Wrapped around each other
And their feet were warm
Where Mouse lay curled up on them

And she thought maybe it was time
So she closed her eyes
And unlocked all of the cells
Let everything free
Let everything roam around her head
Everything she pushed down
Held back
Ignored
Fought
She greeted everything with a timid
Welcome back
Emotions hit like waves
Washing over her mind
And feeling them
Felt like
So
Much
Felt like everything
All at once
Like taking off a blindfold
Turning on a light
Opening your eyes
'I do have resolutions.'
It came out as a whisper
Alice perked an eyebrow
And Beth dropped her hand
And stood up

She took one step
Just one step

And the edge of the wooden
Island
Was
Right there
She could curl her toes around it
One step
And it wasn't enough

She took one step
And she was somewhere new
Two more steps
And she stopped counting
Focusing on the damp soaking up through her socks
The cold tingling her toes
She walked until she reached the end of the garden
And she turned around
And she looked

At her house
The lights in the windows
The plants on the deck
The dog
Fast asleep on the step
The girl
Watching her
With no expression
Just a glow
Like her feelings were too much
To be shown
She looked at this picture

The blankets wrapped around Alice's shoulder
Mouse's blue collar
The door
Wide open
Spilling an orange glow
And the crackling of the fire
And the smell of garlic
Her chest was tight
Her heart pounding
But she looked at her home
From this new place
And she thought
That leaving
Some day
When she was ready
Would be
So worth
It
Just to come back
To this

And she did
She went back
She went home
And she took Alice's hands
And she pulled her up
Wrapped her arms around her waist
And squeezed
And felt her
So close

And smelled her sweet perfume
And she felt like a
Person
She felt like
A Person
She felt
And she was
And she existed
And so did the dog at her feet and the
Girl in her arms
The girl who was crying so softly
Sniffling and smiling
The girl who had done nothing
But be there
But show her
That she was worth waiting for
But
Now
They were done waiting
It was a new year
A new day
They would be brave
And scared
And sad
And they would dance
And sing
And debate
And cook and burn and eat
And read and hold hands
And hold each other

Hold each other up
Hold each other close
Hold each other together
And they would be
Together
She looked at her tear streaked face
And a giggle came from nowhere
From everywhere
From the space in between
And Alice giggled too
The same
Manic
Loaded
Giggle
That said everything they had held on their tongues
And they laughed and they held on to each other and
when they were done
When it was over
They were kissing
And it was
Everything

About the Author

Meg Grehan is a young writer originally from County Louth but now hiding away in Donegal in the northwest of Ireland, with a very ginger girlfriend, an even more ginger dog and an undisclosed number of cats (none of whom is ginger). She works as a stage manager and theatre technician. She has written for online newspapers and journals such as *The Arcade*, but this is her first book. She likes cake and rain; dislikes going outside.